Rumpelstiltskin

A long time ago, there was a miller who lived in a town that had fallen on hard times. The townspeople were forced to pay very high taxes, and the miller was brought before the king for not paying his.

"Please, Your Majesty," pleaded the miller. "I have a daughter who can do the most extraordinary thing: she can spin straw into gold! I can bring her to you if only you will forgive me!"

"This is very interesting indeed!" said the king. "Bring her to me, and you will be forgiven."

The miller regretted his words as soon as he had spoken them, but it was too late. The following morning, his daughter was brought before the king. The king placed her in a huge room filled with straw and said: "Spin this straw into gold or you and your father will be sent to prison!"

Then, the king locked the door behind him, and left the girl alone with the many heaps of straw.

The girl wept and wept—she couldn't spin straw into gold! What was she to do? She didn't want her father thrown in prison! There seemed to be no way out.

Suddenly, through her tears, the girl noticed a small figure standing in the shadows in the corner of the room.

"Who's there?" she sniffled. "Show your face!"

The little figure stepped forward and appeared before the girl. He was an imp-like creature.

"My poor dear," he said. "Why do you weep so terribly? What is the matter?"

"I'm to spin this straw into gold by morning or my father and I will be sent to prison!" she sobbed.

"Today is your lucky day!" said the little man. "I can help you! But what will you give me in return?"

"My necklace," she offered. "I can give you my necklace."

"It's a deal!" said the imp.

He sat down at the spinning wheel and set to work immediately. The girl soon grew tired, and fell asleep.

The next morning, as the sun rose, the girl was woken by the glint of sunlight hitting the gold. When she opened her eyes, she saw to her surprise and relief that all the straw had been spun into gold.

8

Suddenly, there was a knock on the door. It was the king. To his amazement, the room was filled with gold! The girl thought that she would now be free to go, but the king became greedy at the sight of all the gold, and sent her to a larger room filled with even more straw than the first.

"You must do as you did the first time! Spin this straw into gold by morning, or the very same fate will befall you and your father," he ordered.

"This can't be!" wept the girl as the door locked behind her. "I was saved once, but how am I to be saved a second time?"

"Fear not!" piped a familiar voice. "I will help you again. But what, may I ask, do you have to give me this time?"

It was the little man! The girl looked down at her hand. She wore a ring that was a gift from her mother.

"I will give you my ring," said the girl.

"That sounds good to me," said the imp, and he snatched the ring off her finger and set to work.

When the girl awoke the next morning, she was again relieved to find that although the room was bigger and there had been more straw than the first time, every last piece of straw had been spun into gold once more.

The king was pleasantly surprised a second time. He was now growing quite fond of the girl, who was very pretty indeed, but his greed got the better of him at the sight of even more gold. He locked up the girl a third time, but now it was in a tower filled with straw.

"If you spin all of this straw into gold by morning, then I will marry you," he declared.

The girl waited in the tower, hoping the imp would return.
But this time she was nervous, for she had nothing left to offer him.

After a longer wait than the two previous nights, the little man
appeared in the tower.

"Oh please, help me!" she pleaded.

"What will you give me?" asked the imp.

"I don't know!" said the girl sadly. "I have nothing left to give you!"

"Then you must give me your firstborn child after you are married," said the imp.

Reluctantly, the girl agreed.

When the king returned in the morning to find the tower filled with gold, he turned to the girl and said: "Can you ever forgive me? I have been so greedy. Please, be my wife."

The two were married shortly afterward, and lived together quite happily.

Several years passed. The girl, now queen, forgot all about
the imp. One night, as she rocked her firstborn child to sleep in her
arms, an unwelcome visitor appeared before them.

"I have come to collect what is mine!" declared the imp.

The queen pleaded desperately and offered him all the riches
in the world, but to her horror, nothing would satisfy him.

As the queen wept before him with her baby in his arms, the imp proposed a game: "You may keep your baby," he said. "Only if you can guess what my name is. You have three days' time."

And with that, he disappeared.

The queen was very upset, but she knew she had no time to waste. She set to work and wrote down every name she could think of. Then she sent a messenger across the land to gather names from far and wide so that none would be missed.

The next day, the little man returned, and she read her list aloud: "Simon, William, Louis, Jack, Barney…"

But none were the name of the imp.

"Two more days!" he cackled as he turned to leave.

The queen sent out several messengers to visit towns far and wide and take note of every last unusual name. They wrote them all down for the queen, who recited the list on the second night to the imp:

"Frumberbund, Toolioli, Bubbaruba…"

"Ha! Not even close!" said the little man, holding his belly and laughing.

By now, the queen was beginning to lose hope. She urgently sent off the messengers a third time. That evening, one of the messengers returned with an odd story.

"I was traveling through the woods, when I heard the sound of someone singing. I stopped and peered through the trees, and saw a strange little man dancing around a fire and chanting: 'Ha! Ha! Ha! The queen will never win! She'll never guess I'm Rumpelstiltskin!' "

When the imp returned, the queen continued to pretend that she didn't know what his name was.

"Is it Scallabaster?" she asked.

"No! That's not my name!" scoffed the little man.

"Is it Hairylairy?" she asked.

"Not a chance!" said the imp as he danced around gleefully.

"Then it must be Rumpelstiltskin," said the queen.

"WHAT!" he hollered. "But how? Evil woman!"

Rumpelstiltskin was furious! In a fit of rage, he vanished in a puff of smoke, and all that was left of him was the feather from his hat.

RETURN OF A KING

The Battle for Afghanistan

William Dalrymple

B L O O M S B U R Y

LONDON · NEW DELHI · NEW YORK · SYDNEY

First published in Great Britain 2013
This paperback edition published 2014

Copyright © 2013 by William Dalrymple
Maps and chapter illustrations by Olivia Fraser
Tribal trees by ML Design

The moral right of the author has been asserted

Bloomsbury Publishing Plc
50 Bedford Square
London
WC1B 3DP

www.bloomsbury.com

Bloomsbury Publishing, London, New Delhi, New York and Sydney
A CIP catalogue record for this book is available from the British Library

ISBN 978 1 4088 3159 5

10 9 8 7 6 5 4 3 2 1

Typeset by Hewer Text UK Ltd, Edinburgh

Printed and bound by CPI Group (UK) Ltd, Croydon, CR0 4YY